C000137559

*Front cover
photograph
by Paul Carter*

T.F.H.
Publications,
The Spinney,
Parklands,
Denmead,
Waterlooville
PO7 6AR
England

———— • ————

Printed in England

Dog Owner's Guide to
Proper Dental Care

Kenneth Lyon, DVM
and
Lowell Ackerman, DVM

Edited by Susanna Penman, BVSc MRCVS

Your Dog's Teeth

We all know that pets have teeth but few owners have spent the time to really familiarize themselves with their pets' teeth and how to keep those teeth healthy. Some mistakenly believe that animals don't need dental care because they wouldn't receive any in the wild - this is foolish as we wouldn't receive any dental care in the wild either, so what does this mean? The fact that these animals are in our care and are no longer in the wild is further argument that we should endeavour to meet our pets' dental needs, as we do our own. The first step to understanding those needs is to appreciate how the teeth develop and where problems are likely to occur.

ERUPTION OF TEETH

Puppies are born without teeth but the first teeth start to erupt when the pups are a few weeks old. Puppies, like their owners, get two sets of teeth, the deciduous or puppy teeth and the permanent teeth. The puppy incisors erupt at about two to four weeks of age on average, and all puppy teeth are usually present by eight weeks of age. There are a total of 28 deciduous teeth in dogs. Because these puppy teeth provide the pathway for the permanent teeth to follow, puppies should have their teeth checked at eight weeks of age to make sure that the teeth are coming in straight and that there are no congenital problems.

Shortly after the deciduous teeth have erupted, the permanent teeth begin to grow beneath them. Permanent teeth erupt sooner in larger breeds of dog. Permanent incisors erupt at two to five months of age. By six to seven months of age, all permanent teeth should be in place; there are a total of 42 permanent teeth in the dog. At six months of age, a dental evaluation should be performed to make sure that the permanent teeth have erupted properly and that there are no dental abnormalities, especially retained puppy teeth.

A problem that sometimes occurs in young dogs is retained deciduous teeth. This means that the puppy teeth remain when they should have been lost and this can cause crowding in the mouth. As a general rule, no two teeth of the same type should be occupying the same place at the same time. If not corrected early, this can cause permanent changes to the dental pattern. These retained teeth can be removed by your veterinarian to allow room for the permanent teeth to erupt. Radiographs (X-rays) are usually taken first to confirm that there are in fact permanent teeth available to erupt and that they are not impacted. It is also important to realize that the upper and lower jaws grow at different rates and independently from one another. This is a normal occurrence but because the puppy and adult teeth grow in so quickly, they may create a problem of dental "interlock" as the upper and lower jaws grow at different rates. This is another reason why dogs should have dental checkups at eight weeks of age (when the puppy teeth have all erupted) and again at six to seven months of age (when the permanent teeth have all erupted). Corrections of tooth placement are referred to as orthodontics.

TOOTH ANATOMY

The terminology used to describe teeth is similar whether the patient is animal or human. Animals have incisors, canine teeth, premolars and molars. Each tooth has four surfaces and this is important when it comes to understanding the need for comprehensive dental cleaning. The labial surface of a tooth faces the

Anatomy of a tooth. (Reprinted with permission from Tholen, M: The role of the technician in veterinary dental medicine. 1. Dental Anatomy and Pathology, Veterinary Technician 1984, 5:286-291).

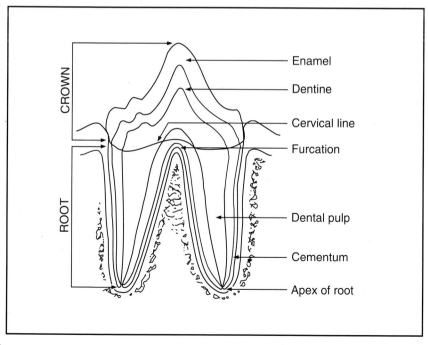

CROWN

ROOT

Enamel

Dentine

Cervical line

Furcation

Dental pulp

Cementum

Apex of root

Puppy teeth are sometimes called deciduous or milk teeth.

lips; the lingual surface faces the tongue; the occlusal surface is the biting and chewing area; and the contact surface is that area between adjacent teeth. When brushing the teeth most of the attention is focused on the outer labial aspects of the teeth because these are most accessible but it is important to remember that plaque can form on all surfaces and all surfaces need cleaning.

The part of the tooth that extends above the gum line, and that we can see, is called the crown. This is the part of the tooth that we can clean at home. The uppermost layer of the crown is the enamel which forms a hard protective covering for the underlying dentine. This dentine consists of dense material and constitutes the bulk of the tooth. It can be sensitive to both heat and cold and therefore needs to be covered by a healthy layer of enamel.

The tooth root is that portion below the gum line, just as the crown is that portion above the gumline.

Cementum covers the tooth root and helps to anchor the tooth to the underlying bone. The central core of the tooth is called the pulp. The pulp is soft and contains nerves and blood vessels. If the pulp becomes exposed the tooth becomes very painful. In this case the tooth can be repaired by special endodontic procedures or by extracting the tooth.

The tooth itself is anchored in the periodontium, which consists of the gums (gingiva), supporting ligaments, the cementum and bone. An understanding of this aspect of oral anatomy is critical because it is in this space, between the teeth and the gums, that pockets develop and gingivitis occurs. The gums are the first line of defence against periodontal disease and this is a point worth noting. In time, if dental health care is not maintained, periodontal disease results, there is

Just as humans do, dogs get a second set of teeth commonly called permanent teeth.

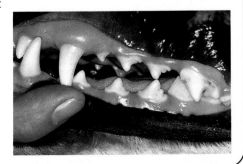

loss of supporting bone, and the teeth loosen and fall out. Accompanying infection can spread via the bloodstream to the liver, kidneys and heart causing other medical problems. Proper home care and regular veterinary dental prophylaxis maintain the teeth and gums in a healthy state so that they should last the pet's whole life.

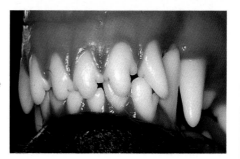

Most breeds of dog have a scissors bite.

BITE

Most people can appreciate that the teeth should meet in a normal manner and certainly there are many people that have worn braces to straighten their own teeth. In dogs, normal occlusion (the meeting of upper and lower teeth) is often referred to as a scissor bite. With a normal "bite" the upper incisors should end up just in front of the lower incisors when the mouth is closed. There are many other rules that apply to how the molars and premolars should meet, where the canines should rest and how the jaws should be opposed when the mouth is closed. If the "bite" is abnormal, there will be abnormal tooth wear, perhaps pain on chewing and sometimes, difficulty eating. Of course some breeds have been created with abnormal bites and this must also be appreciated. Breeds such as the Bulldog are supposed to have an undershot jaw, called prognathism. In most breeds however, this is a genetic fault and the animal should definitely not be used for breeding. The opposite problem is an overshot jaw, or brachygnathism, which is an abnormality in all breeds. These animals should also not be used for breeding. It is important to note that some orthodontic problems are not genetic in origin but result from dental "interlock" when the upper and lower jaws grow at different rates. When this malocclusion interferes with dental function, correction can be attempted with orthodontics. Of course, orthodontics should not be used for cosmetic purposes in purebreds with heritable defects since they can still pass the problems along to future generations.

SUMMARY: To gain a full appreciation of dental health, it is important to understand how the teeth develop and why problems occur in specific areas. It is then easier to understand why routine care is needed and how it benefits our pets.

Proper Dental Care

We learn from a very young age how important it is to take care of our teeth, the necessity of regular dental checkups, and the danger of tartar and gum disease. It is therefore hard to believe that until a few years ago, veterinary dentistry consisted only of routine cleaning procedures, and extracting bad teeth. Veterinary dentistry is now an approved speciality, recognized by the British Small Animal Veterinary Association, and is enjoying much popularity as both owners and veterinarians realize the benefits of routine dental care for pets.

Our thinking about health care in general has changed greatly in recent years. Rather than be preoccupied with how to treat diseases, we are realizing that the key to good health is prevention. This concept is usually expressed as "wellness," meaning that health comes from preventing disease, rather than waiting for it to occur and then treating it. Wellness is more than a fad and it is fortunate that the concepts are being applied to our pets. Unfortunately, although everyone appreciates the need for dental care, most pets do not receive adequate attention for their dental needs and are suffering for it.

It is a sad statistic that more than 85% of dogs older than four years of age have periodontal disease.

Periodontal disease is the most common cause of both tooth loss and bad breath in dogs, and is so prevalent that many people have just come to consider it normal. After all, don't all dogs have "doggy breath"? Obviously, there is a great need for dental care in these animals, but for some reason they are not receiving this care and are suffering from an entirely preventable disease. The process doesn't end there. If periodontal disease continues and the gums start bleeding, bacteria growing in the pockets created around the teeth are released into the bloodstream where they can travel to the heart, liver and kidneys. As if that is not bad enough, chronic periodontal disease results in loss of anchoring bone and the teeth eventually fall out.

As we care for our pets better, and they live longer lives, dental care becomes a more critical issue. Just as vaccinations help prevent our pets from getting a number of different diseases, periodic veterinary dental checkups and regular home care help to prevent periodontal infection, tooth loss, bad breath, tartar buildup, and associated infections. Actually, when you consider that the average person is very aware of the need for dental visits, tooth brushing, dental flossing, tartar control and fluoride treatments, it is amazing that pet dental health has been such a neglected issue. If there was a virus affecting 85% of dogs over four years of age, there would be panic in the pet-owning public. And yet dental care is sometimes neglected even though most problems are entirely preventable. Even if you take your pet to the veterinarian every six months for a dental cleaning, it is not enough. Who would think of allowing their children not to brush their teeth between dental visits? Regular dental home care is as important as veterinary dental care; the reasons are fairly simple.

To truly appreciate the need for dental care it is important to know about plaque and calculus and how they fit into the picture of dental health. Plaque is a combination of bacteria, bits of food, and saliva that adheres to the teeth on a daily basis. This plaque, once it forms, cannot be rinsed away with water; it tenaciously hangs on to the teeth. It can only be removed by brushing or by veterinary dental instruments. Now is the time to remove this plaque (daily) before it causes any serious problems.

Plaque collects below the gum line and starts to lift the gum away from the tooth. The pocket that is formed in this region not only collects bacteria and plaque but damages the attachments that hold the tooth in place and the underlying bone to which it is anchored. At this stage, brushing at home will not do any good because you can't get under the gum margin to arrest the damage. Veterinary intervention can halt the process of periodontal disease if caught in time so that permanent damage does not occur. In time, if plaque is allowed to remain on your pet's teeth, it becomes mineralized and is called tartar (calculus). This hard, rough material is an excellent breeding ground for bacteria, and, unlike plaque, calculus cannot be removed from the teeth by brushing. Tartar buildup doesn't just happen by accident. Dogs that are fed soft food rather than hard dry food get more tartar and some breeds are more affected than others. Small breeds of dogs appear to have more problems with tartar than do larger dogs, and breed types with a lot of muzzle hair such as poodles, schnauzers and terriers also have more problems. Toy breeds, that tend to breathe with their mouths open, are more prone to tartar because their mouths become dry. If your pet does have tartar buildup it will need to be removed, under anaesthetic, by a veterinarian. Do not try to remove it yourself by scraping as you might do considerable damage to the supporting structures of the teeth as well as to the enamel. There are some things you can do at home, and some things that are best left to your veterinarian.

The first stage of dental disease associated with plaque and calculus is called gingivitis. It occurs when the bacterial population around the teeth is approximately 10-20 times greater than normal. At this time the margins

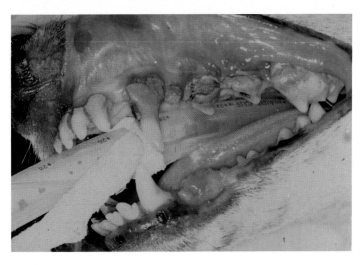

Above: Severe tartar accumulation on a dog's teeth. **Below:** Periodontal disease progression. (Photo courtesy of Petcom, Inc.).

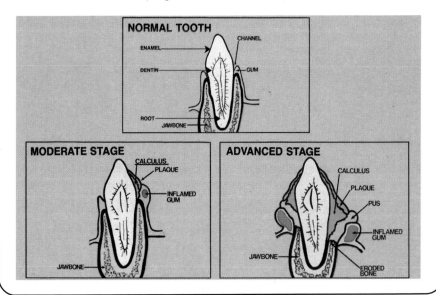

Broken teeth in the dog's mouth should be attended to by a veterinarian. Owners must carefully monitor what their dogs put into their mouths.

teeth. This is often first noted as bad breath which most owners consider more an aesthetic problem than a medical issue. The fact is that infection will end up causing the gums to bleed as well as allowing pus to accumulate under the gums. Owners may never see evidence of bleeding gums unless they closely inspect chew toys or bones for flecks of blood. When a dog's gums are infected (gingivitis), every time the dog chews, the impact on the teeth force microbes deeper into the tissues and eventually into the bloodstream. The bacteria may circulate around the body and end up in a variety of organs, especially the heart, liver or kidneys where they can do serious damage.

The good news is that all of these problems are entirely preventable. Plaque can be removed at home by regular brushing and by using oral

of the gums may become reddened to reflect the inflammation occurring there. Gingivitis may start to occur in pups as young as nine months of age, and can become severe by the time a dog is two years old. Gingivitis is completely reversible with proper veterinary attention and home care. If the process continues however, there is damage to the anchoring attachments of the teeth and we refer to this as periodontitis. Even this can often be reversed with appropriate attention but as the process continues, the damage caused can be permanent. Don't let this happen to your dog - those teeth are meant to last a lifetime!

What if pets do develop periodontitis and eventually lose their teeth? Is that so bad? Well, part of the problem is that pets with periodontal disease have infected gums as well as infections around the roots of the

A side effect of the distemper virus is discoloured teeth and pitting.

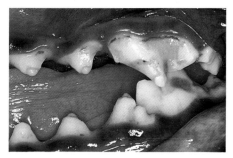

rinses. Regular veterinary visits for dental evaluation should be scheduled every six to 12 months. The dental prophylaxis procedure will remove tartar and even plaque from below the gumline. Pets encouraged to eat dry foods and given appropriate chew toys will also have fewer problems with plaque and tartar.

OTHER PROBLEMS

With people, a discussion of dental health would of course include the topic of cavities. In dogs, we talk about caries, the bacterial destruction of the tooth surface. Caries is more often apparent on the crown but might also be seen in the root if it has been exposed by ongoing periodontal disease. Caries is not as common in dogs as in people for several reasons. Firstly, the pH of dog saliva is different from people's and not as favourable to the bacteria that initiate caries. Secondly, most dogs eat a diet low in fermentable carbohydrates (sugars) which promote the growth of caries-causing bacteria in people. In dogs, caries is most often found in the upper molars which tend to have more "pits" than the other teeth. Also, caries may be seen in teeth secondary to gingivitis and periodontitis where the inflammation in the gums exposes the tooth root to bacterial damage.

Dogs can suffer from broken teeth, most often from chewing on objects that are too hard for them, such as stones. If the pulp is not exposed by the fracture, the dentine will thicken over the pulp to protect it. But, if the pulp is exposed or if the unexposed pulp is severely damaged by the impact (purple-grey tooth discolouration in a few weeks), endodontic treatment (root canal therapy) is needed or the tooth must be extracted.

The enamel is prone to insults other than just fracture. While the enamel is forming, it is susceptible to damage, especially from fevers, viruses and drugs. The distemper virus, in particular, can cause pitting and discoloration of the teeth which is not reversible. Tetracyclines, when administered to pregnant females or to pups less than six months of age, can also discolour the teeth.

SUMMARY: Periodontal disease is so widespread that there is a critical need to be aware of the damage that can result from neglected dental care. Without tooth brushing and veterinary dental prophylaxis, most pets would develop some degree of periodontal disease, resulting in tooth loss and the spread of bacteria throughout the bloodstream, doing damage in the liver, kidneys and heart.

All these dental problems cause pain which is rarely noticed. It is often only after they have been treated and the dog returns to normal that we can appreciate how dull and miserable he has been with toothache.

Home Care

Just as you wouldn't think of neglecting your own teeth between dental visits, your pet needs dental attention more often than once every six to 12 months. In order to prevent gum disease and tooth loss, it becomes important to keep a pet's teeth clean on a day-to-day basis.

Don't underestimate the value of cleaning your pet's teeth at home. Since plaque develops daily, you should begin routine cleaning procedures by the time your pet is about six months of age. At this age your pet will quickly learn to accept teeth cleaning as part of a routine home care ritual. If you're starting with an older pet, don't worry - it may take a little more time and patience but the benefits are worth it. There are several things you can do at home to keep your pet's teeth healthy between veterinary dental checkups.

CHEWING FOR DENTAL WELL BEING

It may sound obvious, but the more dogs chew, the cleaner the teeth become. Some pets are better chewers than others, and it is the actual chewing itself that gets the job done. The longer a dog spends chewing at something the longer the abrasive action of chewing will scrub the teeth clean. On the other hand, if a dog just gulps a biscuit as a treat rather than chewing it, there is very little benefit.

Hard, dry foods tend to contribute less to dental plaque than soft foods, as they are less sticky and need more chewing, which helps to clean the teeth. If your dog is a "gulper," the dry food will probably not remain in the mouth long enough to get the job done. The same is often true of biscuits. If they are accepted as a treat and eaten quickly, they will not work as well as if they are chewed thoroughly and completely. Because many of the biscuits available have more than 100 calories apiece, use them only as directed by the manufacturer; consider also the low-calorie varieties. The advantage of biscuits is that the vast majority of dogs will gladly accept them; some are more particular when it comes to chew toys and treats. One product (i.e., CHOOZ), made of cheese protein (without the fat), poultry meal and gelatin (without sugar, salt or preservatives) is microwaveable and therefore its texture can be varied to suit the individual taste of each dog. Rawhide chew sticks, strips and toys are usually very helpful because they are well accepted by many dogs and the time spent chewing them is much longer (on average) than for biscuits. The longer dogs chew, the more the rawhide comes in contact with the teeth and the cleaner the teeth

Australian Shepherd puppy making the acquaintance of new toys from Nylabone®.

Photographs by
Isabelle
Français.

Border Collie and a brand new Nyladisc®.

Safe toys for dogs are a must for all owners. Flying discs manufactured by Nylabone® are safe for dogs and will not stress a dog's teeth. These Frisbees® are soft and can be caught by the dog without harming his teeth.

Giant Schnauzer chomping on Chooz.™

Chooz™ are edible treats for dogs, and dogs like them. Made from milk protein and chicken, Chooz™ has many advantages for dogs, besides good taste and good fun.

Golden Retriever relaxing with its Gumabones®.

It has been proved by veterinary specialists that the regular chewing of Gumabone® products reduces calculus buildup in dogs. These chew toys come in a variety of colours and shapes, and dogs love to chew them.

Labrador Retriever models with its Nylafloss®.

Nylafloss® is equipped with individual nylon strands that help remove tartar from between dogs' teeth. Gently tugging and playing with your dog with the Nylafloss® reduces the chances of periodontal disease and other mouth disorders. Scientists and veterinarians alike have attested that Nylabone® products make a difference in canine dental health.

Safety and prevention are the keys to good home dental care— Nylabone® has all the right answers.

Bulldogs with toys from Gumabone®.

become. Rawhide appears to be quite safe for dogs and a very useful daily tool to help keep their teeth clean.

Nylon chew toys are also excellent chewing abrasives for dogs. Some dogs love their chew toys and spend hours a day with them; others seem disinterested. They come in a variety of sizes and shapes, from bones to balls to flying discs, to provide dogs with chewing exercise and fun. One product (Plaque Attacker) has raised "dental tips" to combat plaque and tartar and is shaped to reach inner and outer aspects of the teeth. There is even a chew toy (Nylafloss) with nylon strands that functions like dental floss to remove destructive plaque from between the teeth and beneath the gum line.

Give your pet a variety of chewing options and you will quickly learn which ones they spend the most time chewing. Whichever safe products encourage your pet to chew will do their part to help remove plaque and calculus.

An important consideration in the choice of chewing supplements is safety. Do not give your dog real bones under any circumstances. Although they will have some desirable cleaning effects on the teeth, they are potentially very dangerous. Not only can they cause vomiting and diarrhoea, but there is a very real danger that they will cause an obstruction or a puncture in the digestive tract. Biting on bones can break teeth as well. When there are so many safe chewing supplements available it doesn't make sense to risk your dog's health with real bones.

Chewing is great for the teeth but some teeth benefit more than others from the exercise. Since dogs chew with their molars and premolars, these teeth benefit most. The large canine teeth are really designed for ripping rather than chewing and so do not benefit as much from chewing. It is important to stress that the act of chewing helps remove dental plaque. The pet that eats soft food and refuses chew toys needs to have more dental care by a veterinarian and more home care by the pet owner.

BRUSHING THE TEETH

You should be brushing your pet's teeth daily, as the toothbrush is the best means of removing plaque. It's not as difficult as you might imagine and, after the initial fuss, it shouldn't be traumatic for either your pet or yourself.

Step one is to pick an appropriate pet toothbrush. Save yourself time and money by not buying a child's toothbrush for the job - it won't work. Not only are the bristles of even a child's toothbrush too hard for pets but even the shape of the brush never seems to fit the pet's mouth and teeth correctly. The ideal pet toothbrush will have a long handle to give you good access to the teeth, an angled head to better fit a pet's mouth and extra soft bristles to add to your pet's comfort. If you select this or a similar type of brush, your pet will accept the process better and you'll be able to do a better job. Another option is the brush and gum massage tools that fit over your finger. Some people find it easier to "finger brush" their pets teeth, while others prefer a standard pet toothbrush; the choice is yours. Step two is to select the right dog toothpaste. The best is an enzymatic toothpaste that is specially formulated for dogs. These pet toothpastes contain no detergents, baking soda or salt which are often found in human products and that may be harmful to pets. Fluorides may be incorporated into the toothpaste to help control the bacteria that contribute to plaque and to protect teeth from caries. Ask your veterinarian for advice and don't use human products. Once you select your pet toothpaste, take the time to apply it properly to the brush to get the most benefit. Rather than leaving a strip of paste on top of the bristles, squirt the paste between the bristles. This allows the dentifrice to spend the most time in contact with the teeth.

Step three is to get the brush with dentifrice into your pet's mouth and get those teeth, all of them, brushed. Most pets accept brushing if they are approached in a gentle manner. If you can start them young enough, it's quite easy, but even older pets will accept the process if you're

Proper brushing requires proper placement of the brush against the teeth. (Reprinted from Schmid, MO: Plaque control. In, Gliman's Clinical Periodontology, Carranza, FA, ed., WB Saunders Co., Philadelphia, 1984.)

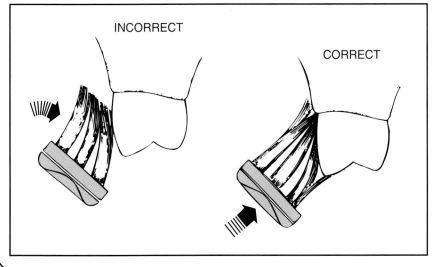

INCORRECT

CORRECT

gentle and patient. If your dog is not used to having its teeth brushed, start slowly. Sit small dogs on your lap; kneel or sit next to large dogs, but do not approach them from in front, as they find this rather frightening. Cuddle them while you do their teeth. As most dogs love the taste of the toothpaste, it is easy to start off by brushing the front teeth. After about two weeks, you will be able to reach the back teeth. If your dog won't accept this, you can use a washcloth or a piece of gauze to wipe the teeth, front and back, in the same manner you will eventually be using a toothbrush. Do this twice daily for about two weeks and your pet should be familiar with the approach. Then, take your special pet toothbrush and soak it in warm water and start brushing daily for several days. When your pet accepts this brushing, start with your pet toothpaste and you're on your way. When your pet has learned to allow you to brush the teeth, make sure your technique takes full advantage of the situation. The bristles should

Antiseptic rinses are an important adjunct to home dental care.

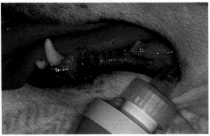

be placed at the gum margin (where the teeth and gums meet) at an angle of 45 degrees (to the long axis of the tooth), and moved in a gentle oval pattern. Be sure to gently force the bristle ends into the area around the base of the tooth as well as into the space between the teeth. Ten short back-and-forth motions should be completed in the same position and then the brush should be lifted and moved to a new position and the process repeated. This cleans the teeth and avoids aggressive "scrubbing" actions. The process should be continued, section by section, covering three or four teeth at a time until all teeth are done. For hard to reach teeth, the brush is inserted vertically and the "heel" of the brush used to generate ten short up-and-down strokes in each location.

Brushing the teeth will be very effective if you take time to make sure the toothpaste makes adequate contact with the teeth and that you do all of the teeth. Remember to get the bristles well into the gum margins and the space between the teeth because these are the areas where tartar is most likely to form.

An excellent followup to brushing is to use dental rinses and sprays that help to reduce plaque and inflammation. As an extra bonus, they also help dogs with bad breath. The antiseptic action of these products helps to disinfect the mouth and discourage plaque formation. The best results are reported with the use of fluorides, chlorhexidine,

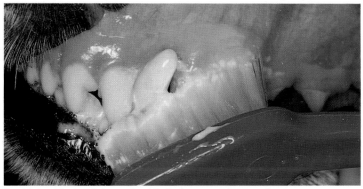

Brushing at home is important to help prevent gum disease.

alexidine, antibiotics, enzymes such as dextranase, and acetate compounds of zinc and manganese. Studies on a chlorhexidine-based product suggested that two daily rinses almost completely inhibited the development of plaque, calculus and gingivitis. These chemical plaque-controlling agents are not a substitute for proper dental prophylaxis. Calculus must be removed from the teeth and the teeth polished before using these agents. Zinc ascorbate cysteine (ZAC) compounds have also shown promising results both with and without brushing. For those who feel they just cannot brush their pet's teeth, this provides a valuable option. The gel cleans and freshens the mouth and is usually well accepted by pets. The product also appears to hasten the healing of gum tissue and to inhibit plaque formation on the teeth. If you really cannot manage to brush your dog's teeth, this is an easy option worth considering. But do remember that it is the physical action of brushing which removes the plaque. This is why tooth brushing is so important. To be truly effective, you must have regular veterinary dental checkups and periodic prophylaxis to help remove calculus (tartar) from the teeth and polish them so that plaque has a harder time adhering to the teeth. Neither brushing nor rinsing will remove tartar but, combined with routine veterinary dental care, will help your pet's teeth remain healthy for a lifetime.

SUMMARY: Home care should include daily (or at least twice weekly) brushing with an enzymatic "pet" toothpaste, and plaque-controlling mouth rinses. Taking an active role in the care of your pet's teeth will help to reduce dental disease, bad breath (which is a symptom of dental disease), and potential life-threatening heart and kidney disease.

Veterinary Aid

As you are no doubt now aware, proper dental care is critical for our pets. It doesn't seem that long ago that veterinary dentistry consisted of "pulling" bad teeth but this has changed dramatically in the past few years. Study after study has shown the benefits of proper veterinary dental care to the health, well being and happiness of pets. These same studies have shown that proper home care, especially brushing and chewing exercises, has immense benefits for pets.

Unfortunately, even daily home care is not completely sufficient for your dog's dental health. Just as you need to go for regular visits to your own dentist, your dog needs periodic visits to your veterinarian. A thorough dental evaluation should be performed once or twice a year and there are many steps in this process. Some of the most important steps are a complete dental examination, the removal of calculus from the teeth, cleaning below the gum line and polishing the teeth. Does this sound familiar? These are some of the same steps your dentist does when evaluating your teeth.

The dental evaluation and prophylaxis (or "prophy" for short) procedure should be done as often as necessary to keep the teeth as healthy as possible. This varies from animal to animal depending on the age, breed, conformation of the teeth, individual tendencies, and the willingness of owners to clean their pet's teeth regularly at home. If you have been doing a good job at home, the prophylaxis will be a relatively easy procedure, cleaning those areas of the teeth that haven't been reached at home.

A thorough examination of the mouth is done at the time of the dental checkup to evaluate problems and to identify areas that might need more attention at home. This often involves using a periodontal probe (just like at your dentist's) to explore the depth of pockets around each tooth. Deep pockets allow the bacteria to have access to the sensitive regions under the gum line. The deeper aspects of the teeth are evaluated by dental radiographs, which can show the attachments of the teeth to the underlying bone. Many veterinarians keep a written history of your pet's dental health on a special chart using graphic symbols to indicate any evidence of dental problems. Like the rest of the medical record, it serves to identify problem areas and record them for future consideration. It allows veterinarians to see at a glance how your dog's dental picture has changed over the years and where problems may be expected in the future.

The procedure known as the dental

prophylaxis involves several steps to clean the teeth, above and below the gum line, and to polish them so plaque has a harder time adhering to the tooth surface. The goal is to slow or prevent the development of periodontal disease by treating those areas that cannot be effectively cleaned by home dental care. Because the cleaning extends beneath the sensitive gum line, dogs must be anaesthetized to do a comprehensive cleaning. While people can appreciate what a dentist is trying to do for them and will allow injections of local anaesthetic and sometimes painful procedures, it is unreasonable to expect this of our pets. While under general anaesthesia, their teeth can be effectively and efficiently evaluated and cleaned and they can later wake up without fear or apprehension. The newer anaesthetics, particularly isoflurane, make anaesthesia, even in older pets, quite safe as long as they are in good general health. If there are any questions about a pet's health, veterinarians will often perform blood tests, and sometimes an electrocardiogram (ECG) before attempting any anaesthetic procedure.

Once the dog is anaesthetized, most of the plaque and calculus is removed from the teeth by "scaling." This can be done manually, but, in most cases the preliminary work is done with sonic scalers that disrupt and remove calculus by their high frequency vibrations. Although many people do not realize this, the sonic scalers don't actually touch the tooth surface to disrupt the calculus. In fact, if they are used improperly they can act like a miniature jackhammer and produce pitting of the enamel surface. Once again, scaling is a valuable procedure because it removes plaque and calculus from all portions of the teeth (both above and below the gum line), removes inflammatory tissue where it occurs, and creates a smooth tooth surface to decrease plaque buildup on the teeth.

After most of the plaque and calculus have been removed by mechanical scaling methods, hand scalers are used to complete the prophylaxis procedure by removing any remaining plaque and calculus from under the gum line. A variety of dental tools are used for this, including scalers, hoes, files and curettes. It must be remembered that the most important phase of the dental "prophy" is cleaning under the gum line. Root planing is used to remove dental calculus, plaque and cementum on the root surface which creates an extremely smooth glasslike surface and helps to reduce the potential for future plaque adherence.

After all of this intense cleaning is finished, we're still not done. We've managed to clean the teeth of plaque and calculus but we need to polish the teeth to remove any rough areas on the tooth surface that might have resulted from plaque and calculus accumulation or even by the scaling procedure itself. The

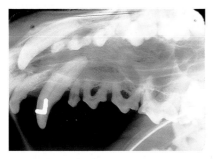

Dental radiographs help identify disorders that may not be evident on visual inspection.

Above: A sonic scaler helps remove plaque and calculus from the tooth surface. **Below:** Polishing to remove rough areas on the tooth surface.

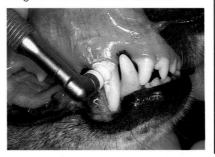

polishing is performed by applying pumice "prophy" pastes to the tooth and using a polisher to rotate the pumice against the tooth. This polishes the tooth surface smooth and helps to remove stains.

After polishing, we're still not done. It's time for a fluoride treatment. The fluoride gel or foam applied helps to desensitize the teeth, helps kill bacteria that contribute to plaque formation and helps to strengthen the enamel.

Anyone who has witnessed a "prophy" procedure can appreciate how long it takes to clean and polish all aspects of the teeth but the benefits can be appreciated by all. The teeth are cleaner (and therefore the breath smells better) and are more resistant to plaque buildup, making home care easier and more effective. And, most importantly, with healthy teeth, our pets are healthier themselves.

SUMMARY: The dental "prophy" is a time-consuming but rewarding exercise in helping our pets keep their teeth healthy into old age. Just like their owners, our pets benefit from routine dental care which should include regular dental examinations, periodic prophylaxis, and regular home care.

Opposite page: A pre-treatment chart is used to keep a record of a pet's dental health.

PRE–TREATMENT

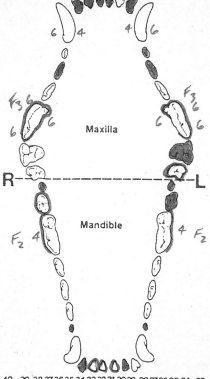

Maxilla

R - - - - - - - - - - - L

Mandible

Hereditary Problems

It should be of little surprise that some dental problems are more common in some breeds than in others. Although some problems are clearly genetic, others are more developmental in nature. Since over 500 different breeds exist or have been created, with different stature, conformation and breed standards, diversity is the expected rule. For example, some breeds have been created that have a shorter upper jaw than a lower jaw and are described as being prognathic. Some prognathic breeds include the Bulldog, Boxer, Pekingese and Boston Terrier. Because of the way these dogs have been bred, all are expected to have an undershot jaw, termed prognathism. This abnormality has become "normal" in these breeds. On the other hand, an overshot jaw is abnormal in all breeds.

MALOCCLUSION

Malocclusion refers to any abnormality in how the upper and lower teeth meet. There are five types of malocclusion recognized in dogs: undershot, overshot, level, reverse scissor and open. Remember that the normal "bite" is the scissor bite, in which the teeth of the upper jaw are positioned just in front of those of the lower jaw. Malocclusion is the most common genetic dental problem and is often a major concern to breeders and those involved in conformation. Mandibular brachygnathism or overshot jaw, in which the upper jaw protrudes beyond the lower jaw, is considered abnormal in all breeds. When the mouth is closed, the lower canines often impinge on the hard palate, causing damage and pain. The opposite condition is known as mandibular prognathism or undershot jaw, where the lower incisors protrude beyond the upper incisors by 0.5mm to 5mm or more. Level bite is another malocclusive disorder in which the incisors meet end to end rather than the top incisors being just slightly in front of the bottom incisors. It is considered a minor form of mandibular prognathism. Level bite is acceptable in several breeds and owners should consult the breed standard for their own particular breed.

The reverse scissor bite occurs when the upper incisors fall just behind the lower incisors. If an actual gap is evident, the condition would be more correctly described as undershot jaw. The reverse scissor bite is called for in some breeds, including the Boxer, Bullmastiff, English Toy Spaniel, Pekingese, Shih Tzu, Boston Terrier, Bulldog, and French Bulldog.

Open bite occurs when there is a gap between the top and bottom incisors (of at least 5mm) when the mouth is closed. It can occur on its own or in conjunction with any of the other malocclusions. Open bite can be concentrated in a line by inbreeding. It is suspected to be a recessive trait but this has yet to be proved.

It is important to note that malocclusion can and often does result from a genetic condition known as achondroplasia, a defect in cartilage growth and development. This is transmitted as an autosomal dominant trait with variable expressivity. For those unfamiliar with the parlance of genetics, this means that pups can be affected if either parent carries the gene but that some pups will be more affected than others. Although the gene pattern responsible for this condition is carried by many small breeds including the Basset Hound, Miniature Poodle and Scottish Terrier, the Dachshund seems to be particularly at risk. It should be realized that malocclusion is almost never seen in dogs that have not been bred by man. We have manipulated the genes of domesticated dogs by breeding them intensively and concentrated these bad genes in many breeds of dog. Wry mouth is another dental abnormality in which an overshot or undershot condition only affects one side of the head, the left or right. Genetically it is a form of brachygnathism or prognathism and is obviously abnormal in all breeds.

RETENTION OF DECIDUOUS TEETH

The deciduous or puppy teeth have normally completely erupted by eight weeks of age and then fall out and are replaced by the permanent teeth. The permanent teeth are usually completely in place by six to seven months of age. If the puppy teeth do not fall out at the right time they can cause many problems by their effective "crowding" of the other teeth. When the puppy teeth don't fall out we refer to the condition as retention of deciduous teeth.

There is little doubt that there is a strong genetic basis for the retention of deciduous teeth but the actual genetic pattern has not yet been characterized. If the lower canine teeth are displaced centrally, toward the tongue, the condition is often referred to as "base narrow." This can cause severe problems as the lower canines bite on to the upper gums rather than the upper canines and cause gum damage, periodontal pockets, and even tracts into the nasal cavity, better known as oronasal fistulae. In the Collie, the tendency to create an elongated head has also produced a more base narrow configuration.

All pups should have dental checkups at eight weeks of age and six to seven months of age to check for proper occlusion and possible retention of deciduous teeth. If caught early enough, the puppy teeth can be removed to make room for the permanent teeth before any real damage is done. If not caught

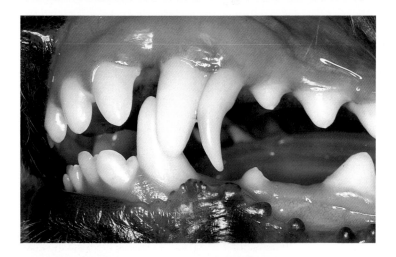

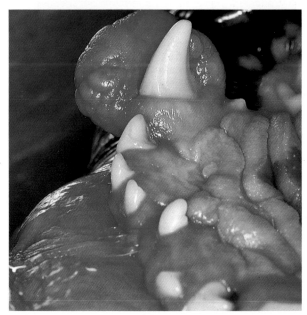

Above: Retained deciduous teeth can be a problem for the growing puppy. Monitor the puppy's mouth regularly so that this minor problem can be corrected in time.
Left: Gingival hyperplasia, the overgrowth of gums, will not need to be treated if it is doing no harm to the dog.

early enough, the displacement of the permanent teeth will need to be corrected with orthodontic procedures. This orthodontic movement should be started at six to ten months of age and may take as little as five to ten days to move the lower canines back into proper position. In older dogs, it may take three to six weeks or even longer. Until the genetics of retained deciduous teeth have been fully characterized, it is suggested that animals with this condition are not used for breeding.

MISSING AND EXTRA TEETH

Missing teeth, or anodontia, is common in dogs and may be inherited. The premolar teeth are the most likely to be missing in the dog. It is important not to confuse anodontia with tooth loss that occurs because of periodontal disease or other causes. Anodontia refers to those teeth missing since birth or in early puppyhood. Radiography (X-rays) will confirm that there is no tooth root in the area and that the problem is not due to impaction of the tooth beneath the gum line. Extra teeth, known as supernumerary teeth, may also occur in the dog and are particularly prevalent in spaniels, hounds, and greyhounds. Just as the premolars are most likely to be missing in anodontia, these teeth are also the most likely to be duplicated, forming supernumerary teeth. These extra teeth need to be extracted if they are causing crowding of the other teeth.

Undershot bite.

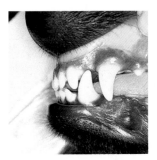

Level bite.

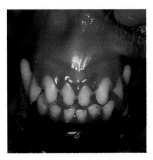

Reverse scissors bite.

ORAL GROWTHS

A variety of oral growths occur in the dog's mouth. Some are malignant and definitely not good news, while others are troublesome, but benign. Benign tumours of the mouth are fairly common in dogs. Of all the tumours that dogs may get, benign oral tumours account for just under 5% of them. The most common benign tumours are called epulis, ameloblastoma, and gingival hyperplasia.

The epulis family (epulides) includes many oral growths, some of which are invasive and some aren't. The ones that aren't invasive may be removed surgically but the others are more bothersome, even though they are not malignant. Radiation therapy is sometimes used to help treat these invasive forms.

Gingival hyperplasia refers to an overgrowth of gum tissue and since it occurs not uncommonly in Boxers, Spaniels and a number of other large breeds, an inherited predisposition has been suggested. Because the extra gum tissue which grows around the teeth does not become attached to the teeth, "false" pockets form which accumulate plaque and calculus and cause periodontal disease. The excess gum tissue is removed surgically with a sharp scalpel or electrosurgery, in which the tissue is cauterized with an electric current. The normal anatomy of the gum is recreated.

The incidence of malignant oral cancers is not high and recent studies seem to indicate that less than one dog in a thousand will be affected by these tumours. The most common oral malignancies include melanomas, squamous cell carcinomas, and fibrosarcomas. It has been reported that German Shorthaired Pointers, Weimaraners, Golden Retrievers, and Boxers are at greater risk that other breeds for developing malignant oral cancers. Oral melanomas tend to affect breeds with dark gums such as Scottish Terriers, black Cocker Spaniels, and Boston Terriers. For reasons that are not yet known, oral cancers tend to occur more often in male dogs than in females.

SUMMARY: Hereditary dental disorders may include malocclusions, retained deciduous teeth, missing or extra teeth and oral growths. It is important to know which conditions may be prevalent in your breed so that steps can be taken to reduce the occurrence in future generations.

Special Procedures

It is comforting to know that a high level of sophistication in the field of veterinary dentistry is available for our pets. Routine dental prophylaxis keeps the teeth clean and polished and even removes calculus from under the gums. Regular brushing of the teeth at home, mouth rinses and chewing exercises help prevent plaque buildup and the development of gingivitis. But what if our pets have special dental needs? What can be done then?

If there is a problem out of the ordinary that cannot be dealt with by your usual veterinary surgeon, you could be referred to someone specialising in veterinary dentistry. The British Veterinary Dental Association (BVDA) was formed in 1988 and has a list of veterinary surgeons and dentists who accept veterinary dental referrals.

Because of the major strides made in the field of veterinary dentistry lately, many of the same procedures used in human dentistry are available for our pets. Some of the major accomplishments in veterinary dentistry are expertise in periodontics, endodontics, orthodontics and restorations. Veterinary dentists may also be involved in a number of different surgical and medical aspects of oral diseases.

PERIODONTICS

Periodontics is the branch of dentistry concerned with the gum tissue (gingiva) and the supporting tissues for the teeth. Most people are familiar with the term gingivitis, which is an inflammation of the gums. The most common cause for this, of course, is poor oral hygiene. When bacteria accumulate on the teeth throughout the day and combine with saliva and food, plaque develops. If the plaque is not removed from the teeth, it will build up and then undergo a process of mineralization. Once this occurs, the plaque becomes calculus (tartar).

The good news is that gingivitis is preventable with proper dental care. Even after gingivitis has developed, the condition can be reversed by removing the plaque and calculus from the teeth, above and below the gumline. Over time however, inflammation of the gums leads to pockets of infection which start to erode the bone that ultimately supports the teeth. When bone starts to be lost, gingivitis becomes periodontitis. Once bone loss has started, professional help is critical, and the destruction may be only partially reversible. Specialized gum and bone surgeries are sometimes necessary to slow the progression of gum disease and prevent the loss of teeth.

Since gingivitis is completely reversible, doesn't it make sense to prevent the problem rather than trying to treat it with less than complete success? Daily toothbrushing at home combined with the routine veterinary dental cleaning or "prophy", which should be performed every six months or so, should prevent most periodontal disease. Prevention is the only way to decrease this periodontal disease and allow our pets to keep all of their teeth for as long as possible, hopefully their whole lives.

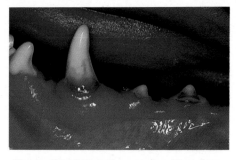

Above: Gingivitis in the mouth of the dog—the beginning of dental disease. **Below:** Restoration of a canine tooth, thanks to modern advance in canine dentistry, is now

ENDODONTICS
Endodontics deals with the internal portions of the tooth, especially the sensitive tooth pulp which consists of nerves, blood vessels, and loose connective tissue. When the tooth pulp is damaged there are two options: pull the tooth out or perform endodontic treatment. The latter option consists of root canal therapy.

The damaged pulp is capped (pulpotomy) or removed (pulpectomy) and then the crown can be restored. The emphasis in veterinary dentistry is to save teeth and not extract teeth. Even part of the tooth can be saved by endodontic procedures so that the crown can be restored for function.

ORTHODONTICS
Orthodontic procedures are used to straighten teeth. Yes, some dogs do wear braces! The principle of orthodontics is that if pressure is applied to a tooth, over time the tooth will move as the bone around the tooth remodels. Since bone does not form overnight, tooth movement is a gradual process. Not every dog with crooked teeth needs orthodontics. In fact, it is unethical to use orthodontics just for aesthetics or on a purebred so that it does better in the show ring. And yet, there is a very real need for orthodontics in dogs that have poorly

positioned and painful teeth, cannot close their mouths properly, or cannot eat properly. Orthodontics does not alter the genetics of a bad bite and therefore cannot be used by breeders as a method of improving their breeding stock. Orthodontic cases in animals require the specialist to have considerable experience to be able to predict the eventual position of the corrected teeth.

Orthodontic headgear used to assist in the reposition of teeth.

RESTORATIONS

When a tooth is damaged but we still want to save it, the tooth can be repaired with a synthetic device such as a crown. A crown replaces the function and structure of a damaged tooth and protects the portion of the tooth that remains. It can be made to closely match the function and appearance of the original tooth, but because it will be weaker than a normal tooth, it will be made shorter. The biting forces in a dog's mouth (1500psi) are ten times those in humans, and dogs like to bite hard on to many things. This destroys most human type dental restorations, many of which are not suitable for use in dogs. Animals' teeth are restored primarily for function, not for aesthetics, and only the strongest restorations are used.

There's nothing simple about making a crown for a dog. Crowns are generally used in working dogs such as police dogs but can be fabricated for any pet that fractures a tooth. Damaged or discoloured teeth can also be restored by bonding acrylic materials to the teeth.

ORAL SURGERY

Veterinary dentists perform a variety of surgical procedures, not all of which may involve teeth. A surgical approach is needed for endodontic and restorative procedures but also may be necessary for disorders of the tongue, lips, cheeks, and palate. The veterinary dentist is concerned with all aspects of oral health, not just the teeth.

One of the most common oral surgeries is to correct palate defects such as cleft palate. Sometimes defects can be repaired but occasionally complete reconstructive procedures are warranted. The veterinary oral surgeon is trained to perform extensive surgical techniques on the oral tissues and skull.

DISEASES OF THE MOUTH AND THROAT

There are a number of diseases that affect the oral cavity and many of these are referred to veterinary dental specialists. For instance, stomatitis which is an inflammation in the mouth, may result from a variety of different potential causes and therefore most cases require careful scrutiny. The reason for careful evaluation is that the ultimate cause can be very difficult to diagnose and incomplete evaluation may mean incomplete control. For this reason, many veterinarians count on a veterinary dentist for help in making as accurate a diagnosis as possible so a comprehensive treatment plan can be initiated.

Diseases of the throat, including the tonsils, pharynx, larynx, and salivary glands, can also be evaluated by the dental specialist. Veterinary dentists may also be involved in the management of oral cancers.

As in most areas of veterinary medicine, there may be overlaps between areas of expertise in specific aspects of oral health. For instance, problems with the lips may be dealt with by either dermatologists or dentists. Also, some oral diseases are related to diseases of the skin and may be managed by dermatologists. Veterinary surgeons may be involved in reconstructive surgeries of the head and face, including the mouth. Veterinary oncologists, specialists in cancer in animals, may be involved in the treatment of tumours in the mouth. Specialists in internal medicine may deal with problems in the throat area or internal diseases that may involve the mouth.

Because of the complexity of oral medicine, and veterinary medicine in general, it is imperative that excellent communication be maintained by veterinarians and the specialists to whom they refer cases. The key to overall success in pet health is the primary-care veterinarian who knows the most about the pet and owner. Pets with oral problems have never had as many excellent health care options as they do today.

Summary: It is indeed comforting to know that veterinary dentists are available and trained to perform such sophisticated procedures as root canal work, orthodontics, and restorations, if called upon to do so.

Index

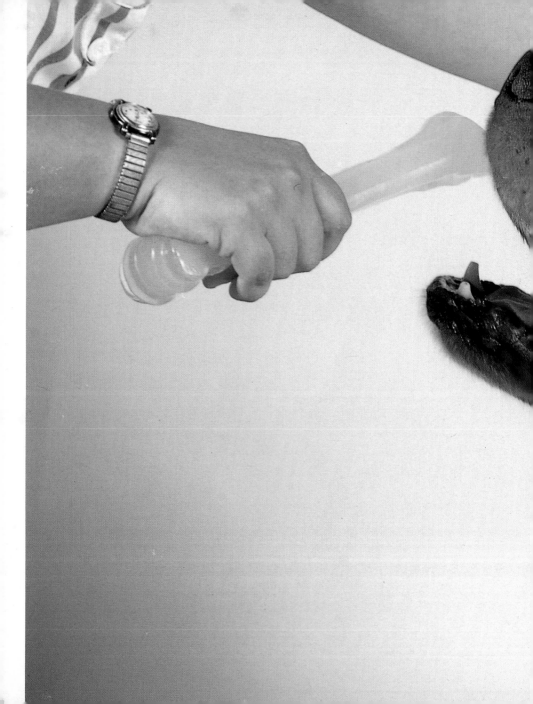